MY POLAR PAWS

Alaskan Animals

Text Copyright © 2011
Illustrations Copyright © 2011
Published by Whitestone High School
PO Box 1229
Delta Junction, AK 99737 U.S.A.

Edited by Nathan Vereide and Verna Miller
Graphic Design by Diane Folaron
Second Edition, Second Printing 2012
Printed by Everbest Printing Co., Ltd., in Guangzhou, China,
through Alaska Print Brokers, Anchorage, Alaska.

Library of Congress Control Number: 2011900544

Polar Bear

I carefully stalk a seal to eat

In a wilderness of ice, snow and sleet.

With terrible claws

and formidable jaws,

It won't escape my polar paws!

Did you know...

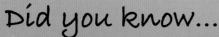

- A polar bear's feet are webbed, so that it swims faster and longer than any other four-footed animal. Polar bears have been known to swim over 100 miles at one time!
- A polar bear's fur is not white.
  Each hair is a clear hollow tube that helps trap the sun's heat in order to keep the polar bear warm. Polar bears only look white because each hollow hair reflects the light.

Salmon

Behind your house,
In a small creek
From pink round eggs
The salmon peek -
Then swim to the ocean
'Til they get the notion
To turn tails around
And swim homeward bound.

Did you know...

🐾 Salmon travel over 2,000 miles to their spawning streams without a single bite of food!
Migrating salmon are able to jump over waterfalls more than twelve feet tall!

🐾 The salmon's sense of smell is thousands of times sharper than a dog's.
A salmon can detect close to one part per trillion by smell, or one drop of chocolate in five hundred thousand barrels of milk.

Squirrel

Chitter chatter go my teeth,
Pitter patter dance my feet,
I scamper up a tree
To eat my nutty treat.
I reach my cozy nest at last,
And wrap my tail around,
Then atop my fuzzy chest
I make a pinecone mound.
I snuggle into twigs beneath
And there I fall asleep.

Did you know...

- Squirrels use their fluffy tails both for balance and as a parachute; as they spring from tree to tree, a squirrel can fall over 100 feet without harm.
- During its hibernation, the Arctic ground squirrel is the only known mammal that can survive body temperatures below freezing.

Porcupine

I'm slow and bumbling,

A fat, spiny fellow.

Prickly and clumsy,

I seem quite mellow.

Just leave me alone

And what's not to like?

But when you annoy me,

I'm likely to strike!

Did you know...

🖐 Luckily for its mother, a porcupine's quills are very soft when it is born. They harden to full strength within 30 minutes of birth.

🖐 Since their quills are hollow and buoyant, porcupines will swim across wide streams and lakes without hesitation. One porcupine can have as many as 30,000 quills.

Wolverine

Slashing,

Snapping,

Snarling,

Biting,

A fearsome creature,

I'm used to fighting.

Did you know...

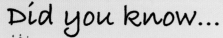 Even though they are only the length of your dad's arm, wolverines are amazingly strong! They can pull the weight of two men!

Wolverines have been known to attack prey many times their size, such as caribou.

King Crab

I am king of all the sea
More than fish or anemone.
With monster arm and jagged claw
I rule the sea; I am the law.
I am smart and shrewd and wise,
Orange shell and knobby eyes.
Lower lives do I despise.

From sea floor to throne I rise.

Did you know...

- The 8-legged Alaska king crab can weigh as much as 24 pounds and measure more than five feet from tip to tip.
- Females can hold up to 40,000 fertilized eggs at a time. A mother crab carries her eggs for over a year before they hatch into larvae, and swim away to become crabs.

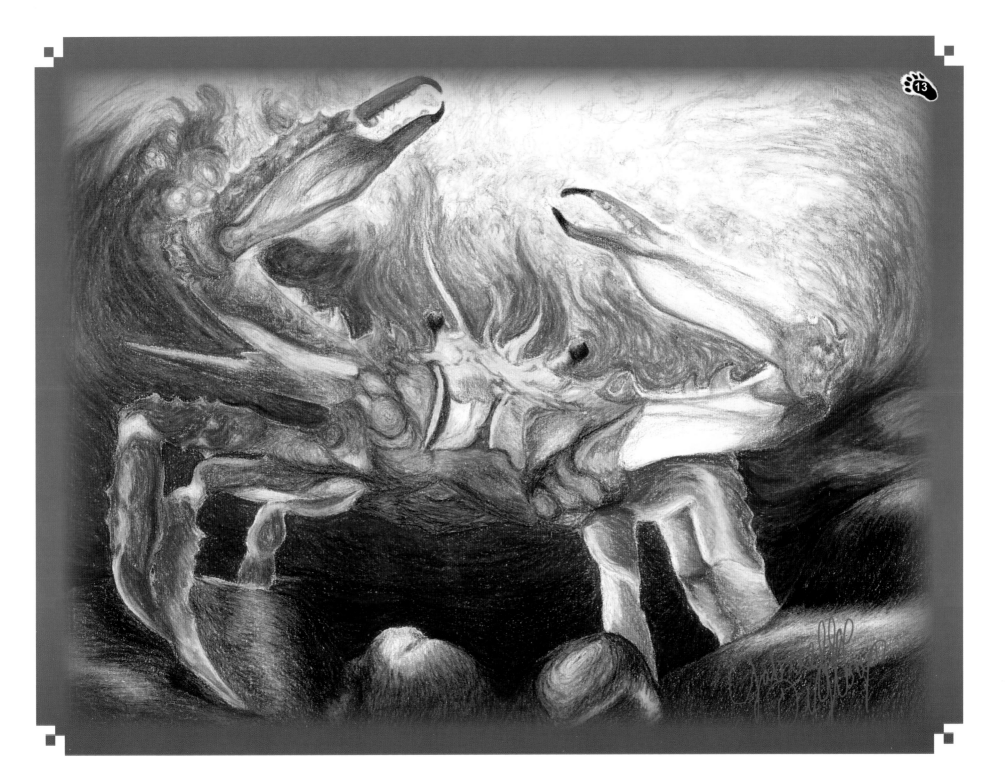

Moose

I have no toes,

Just a rather large nose.

I roam and wander,

Over frozen pond water,

And perpetually plod through the snow.

Did you know...

"Moos" is actually an Indian word that means "twig-eater."
The Indians say that if you dream of moose often, you will live a very long time.

One of the biggest racks of moose antlers ever found was 81 inches across;
one of the heaviest racks of antlers ever found weighed 77 pounds.

Ptarmigan

I watch my young,

Guarding from strangers.

I fight even grizzlies,

Protecting from dangers.

Did you know...

A male ptarmigan is a rare father among birds; he will fight to the death to defend his brood of chicks.

Fortunately, ptarmigan chicks grow with amazing speed - they can get off the ground only 9 to 10 days after hatching.

Their flight feathers are fully grown in eight weeks.

Luke Wheeler

Grizzly Bear

In my cozy den, I snuggle and sleep

While northern lights play hide and seek.

Above me the frozen world reshapes

And to sparkling drips I wake.

My mother teaches me to hunt and roam,

Skills I must master on my own.

Filling my belly with berries and grass

Time for adventure, free at last!

Did you know...

 Grizzly bears on Alaska's coast can weigh over 1500 pounds.

 Though grizzly bears are one of the planet's most powerful predators, 90% of their diet consists of nuts, berries, fruit, leaves, and roots.

 Alaska has over 98% of the United States grizzly population.

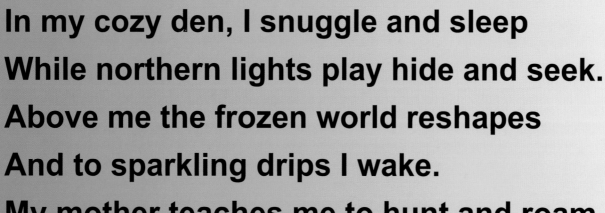

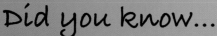

Walrus

Beached on an ice jam,
Cantankerous and fat,
I sleep in the sun,
All day I have sat.
My prowess questioned,
I bludgeon my fellow
With spear-like tusk
And booming bellow.

Did you know...

- The tusks of a walrus are actually canine teeth that never stop growing. Male tusks are often over three feet long.

- Tusks are not just protection against predators; walruses also use the tusks for dragging their 2,600 pound bodies out of the water and on to the shore.

Luke Wheeler

Puffin

On the rocky coast of Alaska,
Down by the windswept sea,
My mate and I are strutting,
Flaunting our fluorescency.

My life is very simple,
Orange beak – my pride and joy.
I dive, swim and catch a fish
To feed my "puffling" boy.

Did you know…

Puffins are great swimmers, but poor flyers. Even though they weigh only 1 1/4 pounds, they must flap their wings at 300-400 beats per minute just to stay airborne.

A baby puffin is called a "puffling." Pufflings eat two times their body weight every day.

A puffin does best underwater, where its short, strong wings can be used to "fly" underwater, while steering with its feet.

Eagle

Riding on the wind,

I am lord of the sky.

I search and dive,

A hunter on high.

Majestic and royal,

Above mountain heights.

I am king in the land

Of northern lights.

Did you know...

The bald eagle has a wing span up to 7 1/2 feet long and weighs up to 14 pounds.
An eagle's eyesight is 5-6 times sharper than human vision.
An eagle can spot a rabbit from a mile away.
When it makes an attack dive, the eagle flies faster than 100 miles per hour.

Fox

Sneaking,

Slinking,

Stalking,

Creeping,

Softly slink and sidle.

Slowly sneak, peek -

and pounce!

Did you know...

- Red foxes are too lazy to make their own dens - they take abandoned wolf dens or steal the dens of ground squirrels.
- A fox's ears are so sensitive that it can hear a watch ticking 40 yards away.

Wolf

I long for night
When only
Stars look down.

I call the pack -

Stealthy feet
Leap and bound
To silently,
Solemnly,
Circle around.

Did you know...

A grey wolf pack travels 30-125 miles in a single day.

Wolves possess upwards of two hundred million olfactory cells;
this means the wolf's sense of smell is more than 100 times greater than a human.

Meet the Authors

This book is unusual in that it has been written and illustrated by not one, but eleven different authors.

All are students at Whitestone High School, a one room log school located in the heart of Interior Alaska.

None of the artists have formal training in drawing; this book is the product of their exceptional talents and hard work.

All proceeds from the sale of this book are used to fund school activities.

Alaskan Artistry

Written by

Allison Wenger, Elizabeth Porter, Eran Eads, Esther Keller, Jonathan Selvaggio, Timothy Chavez, Bryan Woolfolk

Illustrated by

Luke Wheeler, Gabriella DiGloria, Juliana Brown, Stephanie Brown

Timothy

Esther

Allison

Eran

Bryan

Stephanie

Juliana

Elizabeth

Luke

Jonathan

Gabriella

Meet the Artists...

I was born in central Alaska.
One of my favorite things about Alaska is its vastness.
My house, for instance, stands well off the Richardson Highway,
over a mile by boat down the Tanana River. Beyond is nothing
but woods all the way back to the Alaska Mountain Range.
It is in these vast forests that I go hunting every summer with
my dad and brother. And every June, I fish for salmon in the
Copper River, where it is not uncommon to run bears out of
camp. I love creating art, which is how I began work on
My Polar Paws several years ago.
I hope you will enjoy my illustrations of Alaska's animals.
~Luke Wheeler

Caught in the 17th year of my life,
I dream. I am not a typical artist.
I choose to show art through how
I live: dancing to the rhythm of my
brush, dressing my colors, and
painting my dreams.
My contrast comes through mood,
my lines through relationships,
my texture through the bumps and
spikes that life so often brings.
I work everywhere: in a barn, as a
mechanic, in a restaurant, making
cheese, baling hay, helping children.
That is art. Living is an art all its own.
~Juliana L. Brown

Facts about Gabriella DiGloria:
- Plays the saxophone (the only girl in the school band)
- Member of the only Alaska Public Forum Debate team
  to have an undefeated year
- Someday might become a war correspondent journalist
- Loves to play soccer with her older brother
- Very, very short with wild curly hair
- Favorite people: Galileo, Nathaniel Bowditch,
  Michelangelo
- Places to go: Greece, Italy, Denmark, Japan,
  South America, Moon

Hey! My name is Stephanie Lynn Brown. I live in Delta Junction, Alaska, and lead a very adventurous
and interesting life. Working on our book, *My Polar Paws,* was a challenging experience for me that took
some creativity. Drawing animals in color was a new thing that stretched my artistic limits! I often prefer
to draw the faces of people. The sketch on the right is a self-portrait, created with colored pencil.
I hope you enjoy my artwork and have fun reading our book!
~Stephanie Brown